A Complicated Answer

An Anthology of Cardinal Pole Catholic School
Students' Creative Writing

**Cardinal Pole
Catholic School
Publishing**

Published by Cardinal Pole Catholic School Publishing,
205 Morning Lane, London E9 6LG
United Kingdom
www.cardinalpole.co.uk

A catalogue record for this book is available from the British Library

ISBN978-0-9931826-0-0

Edited by Anne Gallagher, Katie Hayward, Raymond Antrobus
Designed and typeset by Kim Richardson
Cover image by Olulade Sonupe
Printed and bound by Bookpress.eu

10 9 8 7 6 5 4 3 2 1

All proceeds from this anthology will go toward future publications and supporting poetry in Cardinal Pole Catholic School.

Foreword

"If our young people grow up holding on to such terrible feelings, it could lead to another war sometime in the future when the fate of the country is in their hands"
                                        Zlata Filipovic

The poems in this book are vital; they challenge ideas many of us have about our young. If we don't give them the space to speak for themselves, we will only enforce ideas projected onto them elsewhere. When a teenage student stood up and spoke this line in his poem, "I am not a mistake, I am a complicated answer," it was a powerful moment that resonated with every teacher and student in the room. It spoke to anyone who has felt misunderstood by someone who is meant to be helping him/her. 11- 17 year olds have written all the poems in this book. They have something to say, something that is as important to them as it should be to us.

When telling people I work in a secondary school in Hackney, they usually say something along the lines of "I don't envy you" or "that must be tough." Media, obsessed with tainting teenagers as criminals, inform negative mainstream opinions of our young people. Fortunately, working with the students at Cardinal Pole and facilitating them to voice their stories and creativity has taught me more about humanity than any newspaper or sociological study. In spite of many challenges that working with teenagers presents, I feel we have established a meaningful educational space for continuous development.

In the three years I have been working in schools, I have come to be inspired by many of our young people. I have witnessed their bravery and gradual process, which gives them the courage to speak out against an adult world that tries to tell them they are unworthy. I am lucky to be able to associate with our young people and to hear their stories and poems that are within this book and beyond.

If there were a realisation of the value of Spoken Word poetry while I was at school, I would have benefited socially and academically. The students who regularly attended Spoken Word Club in 2013 at Cardinal Pole School are from different years and ability groups but almost all managed to move up a level in English, or pass their English GCSEs with A* – C grades.

I myself grew up in Hackney, within a street subculture that wanted to draw me into bad things. In private I was writing poetry from thirteen years old. An English teacher read one of my poems and accused me of plagiarism, stating that considering my poor attendance there's no way I would be capable of writing in such a way. But poetry is what I wrote on my nerve. When you apply your heart to what you write, when you find words for what matters to you, there's a new meaning to what you have to say. You find a power: you become a poet.

Raymond Antrobus, Poet/Spoken Word Educator

"I am not a mistake; I am a complicated answer."

Michael Mchunu, Year 10

Poems and Prose

Under Me

Underneath the bridge is a small goblin and when
it strikes midnight that goblin turns into a giant
and underneath that goblin is a bag
and in that bag is a raging buffalo and
underneath that buffalo is my brain
and underneath that brain is a folder
and in that folder all of my memories
and in that folder is a raging demon
and underneath that demon is a memory
when my dad left me without saying goodbye
and underneath that goodbye is a boy
trapped between four walls
and that boy is me
underneath me is a poem
underneath that poem are words
waiting to come out of my mouth.

Lakaye Maxwell, Year 7

If Ireland…

If Ireland was a man he wouldn't be a drunk
he wouldn't be a conman.
He would be an educated, humble, loving,
    compassionate, honourable and
handsome gentleman laden with culture and folklore.
He would sing you a song.
He would tell you tales.
He would have a cosy accent that some would mock.

But watch this educated, humble, loving, compassionate,
    honourable, and handsome gentleman keeping his
    head up high
as his brothers are shot dead in a sectarian war watch
    with worry
but no pity because he wants no pity.
His ribs bulge as if they are going to explode out of his
weak chest.
He is being starved because of a famine.
Food that he is growing is being given away to the
    British
who could be doing with a bit of starvation.

Try and catch a glimpse of his trembling lip as he buries
    his child
because she was too hungry.
Admire the Irish making lives abroad and striving to
    survive in Brooklyn
because they had to abandon Ireland on coffin ships.

Set your eyes upon the Irish man with the black man
in the street because

they were denied entry to a tavern.
They should have had a red carpet.
They worked all week for their families.
Now they want to relax and have a pint.
They are the working class.
These are the men who made Britain.

Anon, Year 9

Underneath

Under my hair is my brain
under my brain are subjects
underneath subjects there's school
underneath school, there's teachers,
friends,
GCSEs and
stress

underneath my stress is the thought of waking up the next
    day
underneath that me not waking up tomorrow
underneath that is my alarm bell ringing
underneath my alarm bell is the noise of my dad
    screaming
every time Arsenal scores the winning goal.

Kareesa Joseph, Year 8

Name Poem

My first name Aziel is a strength,
it is the alpha and omega of the world
given to me by the soul of my auntie.

My last name Walker is a mark
engraved by desperate slave owners,
it is a whipping
it is a rebellion for their belief.

My name is the power of slaves
it is the bones being lifted up by god
it is the god that gives me strength
it is the soft words spoken by my god
it is the warm water slipping from my savouring mouth
it is the lost story that was written by god
it is the disintegrated love made by slaves
it is the only name I own.

Aziel Walker, Year 9

You Who Brings the Air Out of Me

At Hackney Baths I take a breath
as I dive underwater into a backstroke
I slam my head against a wall and start sinking
you who double-stop the a and e string which thrums a
    chord of panic
bubbles rise as I exhale my vague vision
each bubble a floating treasure chest trying to
absorb the air
the density of the water pulling me to doom
you who screamed for the lifeguard to pull my limp body
    out
you who comforted me on the calm of the poolside
you who fills me up with joy,

as life flashes before my eyes

your powers heal me and I can breathe again .

Tayeb Grace, Year 9

The First Time …

I remember
my First Time being angry.
You were convinced I was a traitor.
With clouded eyes, your pointed finger stabbed me
but now I am at
peace.
The false messiah seized my serene mind
as I was captivated by the arrogant vessel
of madness.
I take a glimpse of the past, its porcelain flesh
and there lies the pure, honest form of radiant darkness
which cowers behind things we call emotions.
The petals of my heart cascade
like jeans, my bleached-out love has thousands of stitches
of sorrows that cry out
raising my gaze, I notice an apathetic intensity
burning and condensing my mind.

In the blistering cold, surrounded by thousands of
    snowflakes
that danced around me
I noticed the imprints of those who'd walked the same
    path.
Mere imprints that would soon fade at the break of
    spring.
Each imprint represented a person with their own
    worries.
The strain on my soul binds me with contempt.
The stain on my soul manifests itself into…
an ugly pulsating monster who wanted to strangle
wrapping my words around you

My hands were vipers ready to snap your neck in two
though I should be prescribed to hatred, I take the dose
I let go of agony; constricting chains
loosened and tightened replicating an intangible force
    toying with me.
That was a moment from a movie of glory.
There are no cuts in our scene.

At that moment the guillotine that slices dreams from
    reality
came down to pass judgement.
In that moment, my human days are mere epiphany
of my own godliness.
In that moment the hell-heat liquor of hatred on my
    tongue was
that moment I became slave of the pedals, gears and
    chains of time.

*Tian Sewell Morgan, Andrew Frimpong, Mohamuud
Abdrahman, Joshua Izunde, Year 11*

The Reaction

It's when it hits you like a boxing glove
a mouthful of death in disguise.
It's when you feel your throat closing slowly
like a trapdoor you cannot stop.
It's when your hands are getting bigger

and bigger.

It's sensing that needle of life hitting your throat
taking that first breath of fresh air.
It's everybody shooting them,
considering
going home smiling
thinking, remember
don't eat that again.

Nathaniel Lawel, Year 8

Goodbye Daddy

We are getting ready to sleep off all the bad things you said to mummy. Sometimes I wonder if it was your evil words that shot mummy down, sending her to sleep in her long dreamy dress, as white as paper and how it flowed with the wind. I wanted to take the bullet for her but I was too scared.

Today was different. You used your words as fire and burnt the house down. You became the Hulk. I saw your veins come; flying up your body like a threatening tank. I could taste your soul.

You filled mummy with sadness that turned into the police visit. A flash of blue and red and you were gone away for good. I knew then I did not have to try to fit into your big pointy shiny leather shoes. I could now be me. I could no longer look up at you. Look up to you. Now, I look down.

I still remember that pain. I remember you. You played us like a game. I can't look at your eyes or say your name. I guess you're just a mistake that wasn't meant to be in our lives. My feet grip the soft carpet. "Is this real?" What we had wanted for so long finally had now come.

Now the police ask questions which are heavy breaths of pain. They question me: "What did your dad do?" I answer, you couldn't love.

Anon, Year 9

What It's Like To Want Someone Back

The day I was born,
he came to see me at hospital,
he was the boat I saw sailing in the harbour,
I couldn't hear or see him,
but for some reason,
I could sense his presence.

As I grew he got kinder,
he had a golden quality about him,
they say everything you touch dies,
but not with him.

Everything he touches gets stronger,
everything he touches becomes kinder,
everything he hugs becomes happier,
everything he loves, loves him back.

Over the years he made me feel something,
he makes me feel special,
the day he let me call him "Granddad JR"
that changed it all.

The moment I turned up at his house,
and he wasn't there,
that was the iceberg that sank the boat,
the boat that sailed on in my heart.

I wondered where he was,
I thought that it might have been something to do with
     the fact,
my nan was crying.

I was told he had died,
but I was six. I didn't understand why,
and I miss him,
I don't like life without him.

Why was it my granddad that died?

Charlie Bail, Year 7

What It's Like To Be From Gambia For Those Of You Who Aren't

Just walking in the market is a task
the smell of drain following you
sitting beside you
dining with you.

To be from a country as small as a pea
compared with other countries
it's a baby

but Gambia is my country

I'm proud of that

Isatou Sowe, Year 7

What It's Like To Nearly Lose Your Life

When I got hit by a car all I saw was white.
I could hear disappearing voices as I lay in the road.
It's like fighting a demon with your bare hands.
My punch had no effect.
I thought I was over but then a bright light appeared,
the demon, turning to dust in my praying,
as I open my eyes to feel

alive.

Nathan Shenesse, Year 7

What It's Like To Faint

She puts her prayers on full blast,
"Jesus, Jesus, help my child, take all the darkness
    away…"
My Olympic weightlifting mum picks me up as I scream,
"I can't see I cannot see!"
She splashes water on my face, trying to wake me up.
Black stars start flickering,
black flowers dance.
Then it stopped.

The second time was exactly the same but it was in the
    line.
At school.
Children would go on and sometimes even tease me.
I was there trying to laugh it off.
The doctor was a lady telling me there's nothing to worry
    about
even though I know it will happen again
I should not react the same way.

Serena Berko, Year 7

What It's Like Being Mixed Race

Curry Goat or Bangers n'Mash?
The full head of hair, not quite straight
not quite picky…a bit of both.
It's getting your hair brush caught in a bird's nest,
experiencing places on either side of the world you're in
Barbados, Benidorm,
big difference.

It's having the privilege to see black and white together
with no problem.
It's looking to my right to see mum eating chicken with a
    fork
and knife
then left to see dad ripping the bone with his teeth.

Rhianna Royer, Year 10

Unconventional Love Story

One average afternoon bored TV and lethargic Book met at the bowling alley, right next to the cinema and library. It was love at first sight. Book was intrigued by the HD of TV's screen and TV was truly amazed at how many pages were in Book. As TV gazed at book, he caught himself running away in trepidation when he read that book's title was called... Twilight.

Coincidently, the next day TV and book bumped into each other on the 277 bus. TV noticed that Book was looking quite dog-eared; she had not changed her cover. TV in fact, was feeling guilty and upset. However realised his feelings for Book were still the same no matter how she looked. She was magnificent. TV confidently confessed his feelings for her and assuredly asked if they could be official. Book, feeling flattered, forgave TV and so they became a couple and found themselves spending the whole day with each other.

However it did not take long before their first lovers' tiff, and there was an argument about whether to go to the cinema or the library. Nonetheless TV knew the convention of "ladies first" and so they headed their way down towards the library first; they went to the cinema as well, but this was afterwards of course. This is where the most memorable moment occurred. They had their first kiss.

A couple months later, Book changed her cover to 'Will you marry me?' And when TV saw this this, he brightened up and his screen turned to a bright blue YES!

So now at this place, TV and Books unite permanently- a marriage of true knowledge. A most fascinating wedding happened and just 9 months later, another phenomenon- we have the birth of an extraordinaire, which is known to millions today -
the Kindle.

Zoia Shah, Year 9

What It's Like To Black Out

I lay helpless on the ground heaving no sound
no hope of being,
lost in the dark devilish hand of unconsciousness.

In my mind my fall is stuck on replay
I really hope I will be okay
what would happen if I don't make it?
I need an escape from unconsciousness.

I open my eyes and reappear in a bed
my mother's soft silky hands bring happiness
I escaped unconsciousness.

Anon, Year 7

What It's Like To Be Shy

Shyness is a cork in a bottle
which blocks your words from feelings,
making you a hushed voice.

It is terror trying to force a smile.
It is the locked back door
I'm unable to open.

Until finally, I find Friendship
unlocking
smiles and laughs

I am free.

Kirsty Andoh, Year 7

Desolation Man

I saw it coming, but it somehow caught me off-guard. I felt a fist of steel clobber my jaw like a rogue freight train. The force of his blow knocked me back a few steps, my feet as dizzy as my mind. My body floated swiftly towards the concrete jungle of ravenous miniature beasts probing the surrounding area for their next meal.

His hulk-like foot swung at me at an alarming rate and cushioned itself between my hips and misshapen ribcage. I gasped helplessly for air but it eluded my grasp. I saw the life pour out of me in a puddle, on the pavement, coagulating in the gutter.

My adrenaline-filled blood started to boil quickly. It flowed out of my lips, dripped down my chin and onto the cracked pavement below. I gathered the little energy I had left and stood up. My fists, almost by nature, locked themselves into place. I threw away the key.

Fight or flight: very simple for most but not for me. Not for us…

As my anger grew so did my fear of losing control, of letting him break free from his prison: my body, my mind.

"Fight! Fight!" the beasts screamed. But they didn't know the risk they were taking, the devastating wrath, vengeance and chaos that I would unleash among them if I were to let go. If I set him loose, the one who took years to be tamed, the one who fears nothing and no one, the one who is voracious for the suffering of others…

Tears threatened to burst out of my hazel eyes and I started to cackle.

At this point I had lost control. He had finally broken free. The beasts were puzzled as to why I was laughing —as to why *he* was laughing. He had taken over.

Pain: he doesn't know it.

Sympathy: he doesn't feel it.

Chaos, anger, revenge and desolation — well, they are his best friends.

He has been locked up for a long time and now has an insatiable hunger for the sweet and sour taste of blood.

By the time they had realised they had made a grave mistake, it was too late. He had taken over to cause nothing but desolation in its purest form.

Raymond Agaba, Year 8

What It's Like To Be An Orphan

It is like your tears fall but have no meaning,
like you die and are revived only to die again.
It is like crying is the happiness of your existence,
and it is like your scared all the time.

It is like you watched all your loved ones die
but have no memory of it,
it is like you are rejected by the gates of heaven.
It is like you live only to be frightened.

It is like your whole life is an exclamation mark,
yet it's a question,
a question that can never be worked out,
a question that can never be solved,
an equation with no answer,
a puzzle that can never be finished,
until…
You wake up only to live that day again.

Marvis Anozie, Year 7

What It Is Like...

What it is like to have an older brother!
Having to argue every minute we see each other
shouting as if we have a microphone stuck in our throats
I feel like I hate him but I truly love him inside.

What it is like to have an older brother!
Who tells you what to do and gets everything they want
never get a chance to play anything or watch TV
just because I'm young.

What it is like to have an older brother!
Who gets to stay up later than you
that think you're an embarrassment
always gets to have his friends over and go to their
      houses.

Elle Landers, Year 7

What It Is Like To Be The Middle Child

It's like butter on toast
nobody really notices you
but
they would hate it if you weren't there.

When it comes to your birthday you are
the star.
But other days, like Christmas,
you're just hiding in the corner.

William Doku, Year 7

'You are the bows from which your children as living arrows are sent forth'
(Inspired by Khalil Gibran The Prophet - *Chapter IV)*

The living room, a hushed atmosphere: so quiet that only the roar of the clock can be heard. Your eyes, a sea of blood. Grief-stricken. You take one last look at the space, reminiscing all of the encounters that took place in the confined area of our two bedroom council flat: the first time I tried to cook and almost burned down the house. We battled the flames together- as a family. I remember the diamond finish of the refuse-sack glistening behind you as the sound of your trudging, heavy footsteps slowly disappear. There's an eerie echo, a creaking sound as the gate closes. You're going away, leaving now Dad. The time has finally come; mother is too weary. Too weary of the frequent fierce, firing rounds of phone calls, that lasted at least thirty minutes before someone decided to hang up. Too weary of going into war to seize a heart that seemed to no longer belonged to her.

Although it still did. I understand that now.

Looking back, I recall the following years. I carried a back-breaking burden too large for my small body and young years. Back then, it weighed so heavy even breathing became difficult. Then you found out about my stepfather, and the struggle began anew: "Let him look after her", you said. Your dismissive words paralysed me with pain and rejection. I could no longer hold my burden. So I let it fall; it crashed down on me, crushing me as if a giant boulder had been sent hurtling down from a height. I couldn't see you through the debris and rubble. My agonising waits for phone calls lengthened. Thoughts wove themselves into my arteries. Obstacles, foreign bodies appeared in my system that knitted themselves into knots, cutting off any emotions; blocking out my heart. I was a small hand-grenade, not yet detonated, reduced to a being of bitterness. I was ashamed of what I had been forced to become. Transformed by you three, I became that child that belonged to a stereotypical Caribbean family – split. Apart. Even at that age, I had my own perceptions on what a family should be. I just didn't understand that things don't always turn out that way.

I understand that now.

I recall one summer; sunshine danced through the debris, penetrated the dark rubble and brought fresh light. Elated at your request to see me, I carefully dressed to look my best; I wore my favourite denim skirt with a lively yellow vest. My brown, braided pigtails peaked out of out of my matching yellow visor. My outfit accessorized with a pearly happy excitement. I enjoyed it. We spent the day, father and daughter, cheerfully celebrating each other's company- greedily trying to repossess all the lost time. It was that day I discovered how love could be shared between a father and his daughter. When the time came for you to leave, you hugged me good-bye clinging, on and on; you wouldn't let me go so I just stood there, suffocated in your fragrance, aware of your love for me. I remember hearing your heartbeat; with mine eventually merging and mimicking its soothing rhythm. I felt your love being transmitted through the protectiveness of your paternal grasp.

Sitting here with you now, you ask me why friendship is so important to me. I tell you proudly that the friendship that you and my mother share after many years of tension and hardship is the reason I am happy. Friendship is the reason that I have access to you whenever I please. Friendship is the reason that, by God's grace, you will see me grow up build my own happiness, as you have.

You made a mistake-yes. You may regret it-maybe. But I'm ever thankful of my experiences.

I appreciate you more.

Chanti Moore, Year 11

What It's Like To Play The Piano

When I was little it felt like practising
until your hands fell off your wrists.
The music pages like one long question
you can't work out.

Wrong notes sting like bees
when I do bad in exams.

Now I can express the beauty of music,
it's like honey dripping into ears.

Helen Wei, Year 7

What It's Like To Have Never Had A Best Friend

It's a dog digging a hole into you every time you lose a
    friend.
It's wandering around the playground alone looking for
    what you can't find.
It's being lonely at lunchtime. Sitting on my own.
It's trying to find a person to tell all your secrets to.
It's walking alone whilst the clouds are moving,
moving, away,
away from you.

Hermaine Bellrose, Year 7.

What It's Like To Have A Future When Someone Tells You That You Don't

I wish my heart was made of steel.
So it won't concave inwards.
So I won't be able to feel pain that's always there.
Hovering in the doorway of my mind like an ominous
    shadow.

Even if you try to think of something else, it's always
    there.
You're kept company by the tennis match in your brain.
The opposition always winning. Never your serve.

It's people saying 'you're never gonna make it'.
It's them deciding your future for you.
Reiterating
over and over.
Engraving their version of your future in your brain.
It's having a song in your throat that can't get out
choking you but you can't sing it.

Afraid that if you make a sound
they will push you back into that cage.
The one they held you in before that broken ball bounces
    back your thoughts.

Anon, Year 7

Underneath My Loving Heart

Underneath my loving heart
is a huge darkness
a tailed beast
and a homeless man.
Inside the homeless man
is a great parade of laughter.
Underneath the laughter is a belly
and under my belly is nothing.

Ever Norena Yepez, Year 8

Your Voice To Me

was constructed from untouched heartstrings
I remember,
it felt so damn real,
fragile enough for love to be broken,
since that moment I knew.

We were walking me and my mum,
walking down Dalston market.

Since that moment I knew
I would rebuild our Lego house
the sky tinted with particles of darkness
whispered by Lucifer's singing
so we could become children
and re-live in a fake reality.

Singing bedtime stories to the myths invented by man
we are stuck in a daydream in our paradise land
where our minds pixelate the farce that stands before us
then I see the reincarnation of the devil-
the Toad Man from X Men
I see fire
and in it the stony desolation
un-pure prayers.

Our eyes meet in the cracks of our relationships
placing his damp rulers of speech upon what I defy as
    beauty
and we know we'll burn together

until our demise
my silent cries
SCREAM for you to give me love

Joanne Williams & Olalade Sonupe, Year 11

The First Time Falling For Someone Felt Like

being cut by the sharp end of glass
drowning in a sea of fear
it's like I'm walking on a thin line
or was it the *thin* edge of glass?
It's like I'm going to hit the ground
BOOM! I'm streaming into my reflection on the glazed
    glass.

I drifted off into a world of horror, swimming in a sea of
    fear
I was standing there, frozen.
I didn't wake with a typical scream, but to end my
mystical dream - I lay there,

my pieces shimmering,
trying to build myself again

my friend taught me how to ask someone out in Spanish
¿Quieres salir conmigo
my friend taught me that the cure to a nightmare can be a
    hug
my friend made me understand her through dancing, and
taught me that salsa was made for two.

We are not invisible
we are not invincible
we are not made of glass.

Caelan Fortune, Year 7, Jemima Williams, Year 8,
Melandra Kwatiah, Year 8

Victoria Park

In Victoria Park, naked trees staring at me,
pointing, bare faced.
Behind me I hear the sound of flickering eyes.
I taste the rubbery squelch beneath my feet
alone, out of my comfort zone.
dressed like a hobo.
Ripped jeans, old tattered shoes,
swamped in a house I called a jacket.
The sky started to cry once I missed my first bus.
The rest of that evening was minging.
I felt like a big boy,
but with fear twinkling in my eyes,
anxiety strangling my stomach.
I marched on.
With earphones (in ear)
I tried to sooth myself with music
I'm covering my ears like a kid. When your words mean
    nothing, I go 'la la la'
trapped in the maze of the words being sung,
my body began to play along
heart on drums
stomach on percussion
windpipe on woodwind
lungs on brass.
Once the band starts to play I can't stop them.
minutes became days.
This seemed to take a lifetime.
Just one last chapter to go
that long narrow road.
where tumble-leaves rolled.

I was blown away,
Literally.

The wind picked up
and so did the pace of my walking
sharp turn left
not far to go.
The band had quietened down once I was outside the
    door.
Just
breathe
out.
In Haringey, empty windows staring at me
laughing at my pain.
In front of me, I taste the rust of the doorbell.
I smell the wet dog of a door mat, smiling at me
beneath my feet.

Javani Brown, Year 12

Peer Pressure; My Killer

Peer pressure is a killer; a murderer of one's individuality. It causes people to do things that they didn't even know they were capable of. Peer pressure can overpower every last piece of conscience. It is a desire to please.

Peer pressure killed me.

'You see him over there? Let's get him. He looks like the sort of guy who'd have a heavy wallet.' They all walk towards him. My conscience tells me not to but my feet have other plans. Peer pressure is controlling me and I am not strong enough to resist.

'Wait. You go first Dan. Knock him out first. Then we'll get his wallet'

If I do this, I will get respect; I will be praised; my reputation will expand.

I run up behind the man and swing at him with all the power I can generate.

Instantly, he falls to the ground with a thud. His lifeless body lies there.

'Oh God- he's dead. I have murdered him'. A belief that he is dead creeps into my mind, but I think of my reputation and quickly dismiss every trace of regret. Now they all come rushing up to me wearing smiles of admiration which I soak up like a grateful sponge.

But I don't realise what is happening behind me. The man slowly gets up, gun in hand.

Raising his gun he aims and pulls the trigger.

Peer pressure had won.

It had claimed another victim.

Peer pressure killed me.

Faith Osifo, Year 8

First Time Angry

You were convinced that I was a traitor, with clouded
    eyes,
your pointed finger stabbed me
and you croaked "Tian it was you who said it."

In that moment I was ugly.
I was a pulsating mutant who wanted to strangle you;
my words wrapping around you;
my viper hands were ready to snap your neck in two.
My chest peacocked its way forward to you.

"How dare you question me when I was there for you,
I defended you when you were being bullied."

Fury gallops my legs to the top of the stairs.
My voice didn't care of how loud and vibrant she was.
She, a green gas consuming the air.
War erupting between us.
Puny humans padlocked their arms around me,
slowly dragging me away from you.

You were lucky that my acidic soul was neutralised by
    the presence of a teacher;
I was once again conditioned with civilised behaviour.
As I paced away, shells of our broken friendship dropped
    softly behind.

Tian Sewell Morgan, Year 11

Stomach Problems

It's like having a person
stab you with a knife
with no pain, no blood and
no death.

It was like thousands of tigers
were in my stomach, biting it (limb from limb),
tearing everything inside me.

It was like my stomach
was the heaviest part of me
pulling me down,
making me stay gloomy
where the sick and the unfortunate lived,
keeping me from home and games.

Doctors staring at me
touching, treating
hurting me
I am powerless
my stomach taking away all my energy.

Then my mum coming to see me
saying I would get well soon.

Joshua Matise, Year 8

How To Be A Poet

Be like me
Never go sleep
Keep work neat
Don't tweet your ideas
You will speak- keep contact
With rhymes in your sleep
Calm down
Waste time
Talk life
Remember you don't just learn through text books
You have to speak out
Shout
Talk crazy
Eat skittles, read books with quizzes and riddles
When you hold a pen
You will be forced to squiggle

Kai John, Year 8

Lost

We raced down the concrete stairs, our feet stumbling beneath us. Waves of people washed past, they knew exactly where they were going. An announcement rings in my ears, bouncing off tiled walls, invading the silence of the resting orchestra that is my ears. It's in French, I don't understand. The train begins to fill up – like hundreds of pots of tea awaiting us back home. I watch as each carriage is crammed with foreign faces, doing the 'awkward smile as I squeeze next to you'. We wade through masses, attempting to make our way to the front of the platform. It seems to be a forest; the ground covered in feet – roots there to trip you up.

Following their lead, I scram to the nearest door, and watch my family, one by one, slide into the sardine can. More announcements. Infuriated French people attack me with roaring words – scold this stupid tourist and her slow reactions. Just as I begin to lift my leg, a high pitched beeping infiltrates my senses. What had I done? Is this what the announcements were trying to tell me – was I about to be bombarded by French police? I looked around, completely dumbfounded. The beeping grew louder. Panic overcame me. I looked towards my family for help – only to find the backs of their heads disappearing, slowly being sucked into flock. Two doors, about to slice me apart; permanently separating me and my family. I watched in horror as the doors met. In desperation I attempted running to the next set, only to find they were closed too. The train began to move, trudging forward along the tracks. As I watched my reflection repeat in different shades of moving metal and glass, until eventually it had vanished with the last carriage. Blood rushed to my head. Anxiety rippled through my body, making itself at home in my frantic mind. My feet stood frozen. A face managed to break the surface of the crowded train. I remember it clearly: my mum's – giggling as she spotted the sheer terror leaking across my face. It was incomprehensible; I was alone, and would never see her again. Yet she found this funny?

Thousands of thoughts splattered across the canvas of my brain, colours blurring into each other, a palette of confusion. The drama queen within me began to fabricate headlines of newspapers: 'Nine year old girl lost in Paris', 'Girl never to see family again', 'Traumatised child lost at age nine'. I tried to rid my mind of these thoughts, but they were overwhelming, and without warning tears began to knock on the door of my eyes, forcing their way out. Suddenly, I felt a warm hand rest on my shoulder. I spun round. My mind a fractured puzzle, completely disorientated. Exhausted; fed up with all the commotion, I longed to be back home (or at least for the day to start over). Standing in front of me, his smile bordering on infectious was my brother. After the initial gun shot of relief, further confusion dribbled across my tear- stained face.

I was having what my friends call 'a blonde moment'. It took me a while to register how he could possibly be stood here with me, if I was certain I saw everyone climb on the train (which clearly they hadn't). He hugged me, supressing his laughter in an attempt to comfort my speechless self.

We sat down on the now practically empty platform, and waited patiently for the next train. By now the realisation of simply how ridiculous my behaviour had been, began to settle in. As the metallic armour glided silently into the station, followed by more dreaded deafening announcements, we stood up ready to greet it. The doors opened. French music echoed around the small carriage, rippling from the accordion that accompanied our journey.

Mae Slade, Year 10

Femininity

One. It was the first time I went to Nigeria. My superficial homeland. It was really hot and I felt even hotter with my face of embarrassment when people found out that I couldn't speak Yoruba and mistook my accent for American and mocked me. They thought because I couldn't speak it, that I couldn't understand it.

Two. It was the first time I felt my own independence. I washed my own clothes by hand, cooked my own food by hand and defended my own pride by mouth. They didn't seem to like that for some reason. I was mouthy, loud, brassy. I was black. I was Nigerian. I was one of them.

Three. It was the first time I walked to school by myself. 2 miles and back each day. I hated my uniform, I wore a dress and I much prefer trousers as you can see. I walked with the turning of the earth. Gravity kept me down and the axis kept me moving.

Four. It was the first time I learned the word 'koboko', the Yoruba word for cane. They went hand in hand and ironically I received it a lot on my left hand, so I'd write with my right hand. They were wrong. My teachers always wanted me to speak. They liked my accent. They didn't like the words that came out of it.

Five. It was the first time my heart was broken by a teacher. I got the highest in my class in PE. I was so proud. I loved PE, the equality of the teams reminded me of home. My teacher, however, shouted at me, saying how could a girl, *a foreign girl* at that, be the highest in the class? He disregarded me. He made me feel invisible. He made me feel ashamed of my work, my reward. He made the boys glare at me with their pulsing hands after receiving beatings because I emasculated them. It was the first day I realised that a spotlight is not about the light it shines, but how it makes everything around it dark.

It was the first time I realised my role as a woman.

I wasn't to play basketball. I wasn't to have friends who were boys because it was 'un-feminine.' I was to be an object of servitude, a thing to be over-looked. It was a man's world. I remember my 12th birthday, where everyone said 'happy birthday' to Daniel before me. I remember the time I swept our 16 bunk-bed room 16 times to teach me a lesson when I said I didn't want to be a housewife. It was the first time when I knew that only I could make myself happy and I would be a Daniel as well as an Abigail.

Abigail Ajibola, Year 12
(Daniel is my twin.)

Dear Gangster

It's your tag name versus abilities. You can't have both.
It's now time for eviction
and your instinct is to kick out your abilities
for a tag name career
but still
you're outchea

This wouldn't be a problem if it was just you ….

But it's the negative influence that you add
and when asked what is the problem in society, you say
    it's society stereotyping you.
I understand it feels like society confines you to its four
    walls of laws and its ceiling of oppression
but you can't run from this reality we all have to face it.
So if the problem is society stereotyping you
"Change that, or better yet change your attitude."

But if you are acting this way for a name
let's just say, this will be my first time expressing my
    intentions for the youth
of this nation who want to be feared to be respected.
See, you come out like Robin Hood.
when you're really robbing the hood
of success.
They're stuck in this 'hood mentality'
where 'gangster' is a state of mind
gang signs, knives are respected

"School? Nah G, I'm out here repping,
soldier for the crime"

believing that they're right, they're destined for
    destruction
I just want to stop this
because as you know, this is not progress.

So this is me for the first time collecting
all the stabbings,
all the years,
all the blood,
all the candles,
all the sirens,
all the mother's tears and father's tears,
all of my brothers, all my sisters.
Collecting to make you understand that
you paralysed them unknowingly,
just to tell them "I've got your back G!"

But when it's time to get up and move independently
they can't stand on their own two feet.
Because you've paralysed their abilities.

So next time you think you're a recruitment agency
realise potential,
advise them that crime is not the lifestyle worth living
just a nightmare with freedom.

Yours Sincerely

Patricia Acheampong, Year 13

A Pencil Is An Amazing Object

Showing sharp points, making paper exotic
like luminous lightening striking
white snow.

A pencil is pictures turning real.

Pencils draw expressions of yourself.
Just using precious pencils free the paper
as you lay it down.

Toyin Agbaje, Year 8

Blurred Lines

This is who I am!
What's it like to be singled out
just because of your talents and intelligence?

What's it like to have a long surname
that nobody can pronounce.
To have a sister
that seems like a stranger to you (with mood swings)

With all of these things I think to myself
what do I have to do to get noticed?
Rage boiling my blood,
desperately wanting to blurt out the answer
but I just don't know when

Putting my hand up
knowing piercing eyes are questioning why
to be purposely sat at the back of the class
no one listening to me!
All that's coming out are blurred lines

a close-in-age well-bonded sister
straying away from everybody
yet ends up staying

banging my head on the table,
my wings finally coming out
I'm able to speak
gladly and finally I no longer blur lines

Anon

Bullets – Malala

Beat down with a single bullet.
Since when did FEMALE mean no, you CAN'T DO
   THIS?
Rising from the oppressive abyss of a failed assassination
an attempt to conform the non-conformist power of
   knowledge formed through education.
They say knowledge is power, right?
Because it's on that 'ledge'
we build our understanding
the true meaning of good and bad and right and wrong.
So surely we must know
that we've lost our way on that narrow path of good
   through evil
when a future female leader gets turned into a young
   housewife.
A child.
Turned into a mother of two.

Admiration.
For the girl who took a bullet for education.

Princess Ashilokun, Year 12

'They Threw words like Stones'

October 2006. The first day at school, I know I'm a late starter, aged 9, but still in search of life's essential weapon-knowledge. My first chance, maybe my only chance, to kick-start my education. Nervously strolling down the pathway I cautiously approach the school's eroding front with my hand in my mother's as she whispers: "Now, you do your best son". I make it to the playground wearing that green jumper I would later despise. As I enter my classroom for the first time, thirty pairs of eyes, as if synchronized, make their trajectory in my direction. Miss M 'invites' me to take a seat. The first day. Trip day. To a place where my father works. I tell them but no one seems to care. Just eye rolling and teeth kissing.

A few days in now, and still, as usual, I've got no one to talk to or to laugh with. No friend. I sit alone, scared, unsure as I watch hundreds of children in the opposite of my psychological position. I spot a group of lads that look more like a wolf-pack hungry and in search for new prey. With their fists clenched and eyebrows pointing diagonally I shrug my lean little shoulders in the hope they don't acknowledge my vulnerable self. I catch the attention of one wolf and they begin to surround me like the walls of a prison. With my heart in my throat the silence is broken with a question. "Hey, what's your bloody name?" I stay silent. The question is repeated, this time louder. "Hey, you! What's your name?" Reluctantly I mumble the name that the whole class would see as 'worthless'. My name. The wolves build up laughter. I dare not to join them. One steps forward, clenches his fist, pulls back and then... I black out. Very shortly after

I am awakened by what feels like five pairs of ten indented sledge hammers forcing their way through my body, but finding no entry. Twenty repetitive minutes later I am lying in the cold hard ground with red soaked patches on my torn green jumper. Bright purple takes over my skin colour, arms, chest and face.

I look back on it now and am still emotionally unstable to even replay slides from these memories that I wish could just be deleted from my mental storage. This will stay with me for as long as I live. Some say it's a reflection on my childhood (the anger). Wait… what childhood? Every day in that school I felt an unneeded loneliness - I didn't even have a single friend to share a single problem with. As I now walk past that school I can't help but relapse; child abuse inflicted by other children. Day in day out I was beaten. Scars came more often than praise from my teacher. I faced this every day at primary, for my money, lunch and for no reason. I got so scared to go for lunch, I would rather skip it. And that's what I did to the extent that I barely ever ate. I became so skinny my joints were the only thing representing my small physique. With my grades appalling, clothes torn, one eye darker than the other and my stomach empty, I would limp my way to the next lesson. And yet the cause of all my suffering was down to the fact that my skin pigments didn't meet up to the social standards to people like the wolves. They were all darker than me. Or to them I was just 'that white kid'. And then there's Miss M, the very teacher who shot down my confidence as if it were a deer in hunting season. Six little words were all it took: "You are not going to be anything."

Barrington Sunderland, Year 11

Who Lies Within Me?

He wasn't the son of an innocent woman,
he was the son of a bitch!
My life and everything around me refused to emit
my inner being
which guarded my faith, morals and all things ephemeral
my only source of light.

Sabrina Yamoah-Afrifa, Year 12

Fear

It is a deep dark forest that will never end
It's being lost in space, succumbing to the horror of the
    infinite universe
It's white noise eerie, away in my frightened mind
It's warm blood dripping down the side of my neck
It's biting into the edge of a Nokia charger with the
    electricity switched on
It's inhaling burnt toast

Kamil Ceylan, Year 10

It Doesn't Bother Me

Here is my bedroom, a quarter the size
of the smallest school classroom.
Here I sing with my twenty eight year old sister
Here I sing like a giant caged bird forced into a miniature
    room.
Here it sings until I am unaffected by the words of my
    father,

with the weight of boulders that drag me down.
I sing loudly to my lungs' capacity and it doesn't bother
    me.
And it doesn't bother me that I sound like pain and
    agony.
It doesn't bother me this will be the last time I see my
    sister
It doesn't bother me that my 28 year old sister is
    almost 30

with the mind of a small child because of her disability.
It doesn't bother me that the life inside her stomach, I see
as a curse but she sees as a miracle.
It doesn't bother me that my father refuses to see that is
    not
and cannot always be right.
It doesn't bother me that my brother sees basketball
as the only escape from the reality that he can never be
the perfect carbon copy of my dad, just as my father
    wants.
It doesn't bother me that my mother is the worn-down
battered rope that tries to use its last strength to pull us all
    together.

It doesn't bother me that my thoughts and understanding
of my surroundings will be forever forced inside
my small room.

Nothing can bother me. Nothing will bother me.
Let the music play.

Anonymous, Year 10

Waiting For The Inevitable.

If innocence were a tangible thing, it would be Jordan. He has been diagnosed with cancer, the silent enemy. With the streaming sunlight wrapping around us, a stern silence hangs suspended in air. It's oppressing us with urgency.

Jordan's mud-brown eyes gleamed brightly in this veil of light as the dismal truth was liberated from his mouth. 'I haven't got long left, but it...will be okay.' This crowded sanctuary, which once carried the aroma of laughter, joy and sweat, was now engulfed in shock and sadness. Our young minds were invaded by a dark shadow. A void, a black pit of despair filled my heart and longed for another reality. Like a fool, my mind reluctantly leads me to the words, 'you're joking right?', but I already knew he wasn't. It was like the grim reaper had visited with the intent of waiting, waiting for the inevitable.

Again, my mind searched for options to go about, what was meant to be another trivial day of playing video games, now it wondered for visions of a best friend's last day in hospital. Jordan looks around with the greatest smile imaginable, and looking back at him I could only stare and reminisce about the memories we shared. I couldn't bring myself to look at him any longer. I ran out. Tears broke through the gates I held up and trailed down my face, I hoped no one saw.

That lonely night, I dreamt of the days we spent. I remember the time where we were so little with no money for Yu-Gi-Oh cards, so you drew me my favourite. The blue-eyed white dragon was shambolically drawn and awfully coloured, but it meant the world to me. I giggled at the crayon marks that draped all over the small stacked piece of card. The smell was still raw and brought me into a trance for a while. You promised me the real one soon. However, I still treasure that card more than the promised one because not only was it dispatched from your heart, it signified so much more.

Our bond... Jordan and I were always close, stuck to each other all the time, even in the cold foggy sea of hatred that surrounded us. Twenty light years away, in the burnished planet far, far away where the skies are made of diamonds, we travelled the stars and had tea with little green men. It's astonishing knowing that we conquered so much and now you're vulnerable to a deadly cancer.

Being only thirteen at that time, I was so immature and stupid. I hope that you can understand that all I wished for was to be able to understand the burden you carried and faced. I want you to know that I'm sorry that I was so afraid, sorry that I abandoned you and left you there in your death bed where I couldn't face you like the best friend you deserved. Like the monsters in the closet, I just couldn't do it. If time was something you could grasp and manipulate I would do so just to see you and say goodbye.

I'm sixteen now. They say you died with a smile. It was just like you to go in that way, cool as ever. They also say that you forgave me for not visiting and saying bye. I can only assume that and be able to continue on living with myself. Life now is as good as the dreams we dreamt of. Everyone's doing well and now and then we visit you and just hang out. In the nights where sleep just doesn't work, I think about what we'd do in the morning after. I hope you're watching over us, my friend. For the last time, forgive me Jordan.

Kevin Tran, Year 11

When Is A War Not A War?

When they turned my home into a battlefield and
left mines in the minds of my brothers.
For Freedom and Honour!

...those were the routine lies shot between our ribcages
with the hard edge of their AK.47s and left to fester.
Till like broken stallions they sapped our spirit
and snapped our pride.

We are mere skulls of our former selves.

Hermits.
Forced to flee from all we've ever known...into the
unknown.
The colours of my childhood were the first to take flight
when war came trooping in.
I guess that means red lost the race 'cause that's all I see
now.
Like refugees it swamps the streets,
vying for room on those rare havens of unpainted canvas.

I heard war makes monsters of men.

Does it?
Or does it illuminate the face of the dark
monster already lurking there?

Princess Ashilokun, Year 12

Rise

Starting from the bottom and working my way to the top.
Tick tock,
like a clock, I cannot be stopped.
Growing up on these blocks is hard enough; put down by
    society, shunned by
MPs, this is our visual reality.
Gun crime and blood stain the streets of what used to be
    a happy community: one unity.
People being shot without a thought for the families
    being ripped apart, like the heart of the last victim to
    these streets, our streets, of Hackney.
But there are those still climbing, rising above the sea of
    blood and violence, upon the shores of hope and
    ambition.
Still fighting to be more than the streets they left behind.
That's why I'm still trying, still rising,
To sit upon the thrones with those who succeeded before
    me.

Marko Boateng, Year 9

Prayers For Hope

Prayers for those who seek the guidance of Auden's
    'affirming flame'
Prayers for those who feel attacked, hindered or
    restrained
Prayers for those who no longer see a reason to carry on
Prayers for those who adhere to disappointment and
    confusion
Prayers for those whose depression clings on to them like
    chewing gum to a shoe-sole
Prayers for those requesting reassurance
Prayers for those who feed the bird of hope
Prayers for their feathers falling in the broken boughs of
    their lost yearnings
Prayers for those who don't know where to find meaning
Prayers for those who want to repair the broken wings of
    their fallen dreams
Prayers for those whose ambitions are smashed, who hear
    the singing bird of hope

Albert Caulker, Year 12

Dispatches from the Heart

'Daddy, Daddy ....I'm through' from Daddy *by Sylvia Plath*

I sit there, helplessly, in the back seat of your car. The 'happily ever after' ending you promised me slowly slips away some more, and the more it drifts away, the more I feel as if I will never fit into this world. I wish things could be different, that we could just be normal. You inform my sister and I about the new woman in your life and I can't help but let my guards down, I can't help but allow tears to escape from my eyes. It hurts. Your hand gently reaches out from the driver's seat and comforts me, asking me why I'm upset. "Why can't you and mum just be together?" I ask, struggling and gasping for breath whilst being buried in these tears. Why is it that all my friends are able to enjoy something they see as normal but that seems like such a privilege to me? To have both parents under the same household faking, if not playing happy families.

"Your mother and I are divorced, darling. That's just how it is." A rush of silence fills the enclosed space, an icy hurricane, swirling me around. I'm helpless. My tear-blurred vision mists my eyes; through the back passenger window, everything is wobbling and seems to be shrinking. I begin to rely on my other senses, acknowledging the cheap smell of air freshener and the feel of my damp fingertips from playing with the water vapour on the window. It's as if I can taste the bitterness of your words, and no matter how much I try, I can't get the taste out of my mouth. It's overpowering and revolting; like that time mum insisted I tasted boiled courgettes so I could be healthy.

After that evening's event, weeks pass and I fail to hear even a word from you. Weeks turn into months, months where I wait impatiently with an unhealthy longing for my 'amazing' absent father to pick me up from school one day, buy me an ice cream on the way home and ask me about what I did in school that day, for my 'amazing' father to acknowledge my existence. Back then I thought we meant everything to you. Looking back now, it hurts to know that you once meant so much to me. It hurts to know that I once loved you.

Sometimes I think I would do anything to see you again, just to ask you why. Why have I spent ten hope filled birthdays wondering whether this time you'll come and visit? Or this time you'll call? If you could know the depth of each birthday disappointment, each silent phone being watched, perhaps you'd have behaved differently. But it's too late now, dad. Sometimes I wish everything had been different, other times I wish you'd rot in hell for allowing my sister and me to pass through life without you, a father figure to have taught us how to ride a bike, or to have helped us with our homework, or to have boasted about our good grades, or read to us at night. It hurts. The fact that you were able to help bring two children into this world and you allow yourself to go day by day without knowing anything about us at all astounds me.

Well daddy, I wish you could see me now. I wish you could see my amazing grades, my wonderful family and my happiness. All three achieved without you.

I still remember your birthday, daddy. And once, a few years ago, mum even asked whether we wanted to send you a card. Part of me wanted to and then I remembered the pain I used to feel each year when you denied me a card or a call. I want you to feel that pain. I want you to know that if I saw you, I wouldn't even give you a second look. I think of all the issues I've had to deal with without a father's support. Without you. You went away. I don't know about you, but I'll get my happy ending, I'll live happily ever after without you. See the thing is Daddy, it used to hurt. It used to hurt more than you could ever imagine. Not anymore.

Talaya Zafar, Year 11

The Banker

Mama told me I had to practise my English.
Don't mind me writing in such an alien language.

There was a Genesis today.
Small silvers, caught in the rays of light
produced by the sun as it fell from the sky.
Machetes paused in mid-air
eyes of greed looked up in thirst.
Children pointed, mouths agape
but careful not to choke
on the rounded objects or take it for granted.

We – me and mama – on our way back
from a church meeting. She, telling me the tale
of a man who, despite not wanting to leave
his world behind, bought himself freedom;
a small coin hit my hand laced in hers.
Every expression was the same. All but mama's.

See, mama's afraid of the Revelations.
She sees it as too good to be true.
She would have taken herself into the shack
that papa had made from parachutes and iron.
She rebuked anyone who picked up any amount of
money. She has seen the bad side.
Her ivory eyes experienced too many false wonders.
Her heart has felt too many shocks and disappointments
and too much mourning for her to care anymore.

And so at the dash to get the biggest bucket
to collect the most diamonds,

she tightened her grip on my hand
and leads the way in the opposite direction.

The diamonds began to overflow the buckets
turning the ashy ground platinum.
There was no way of escaping.
She put down the bank full of coppers
that had been resting on her head,
she clamped her hands around my shoulders,
the platinum grew in size and spilled around our ankles.
She told me that there was a little mine
with the necessary amount of small coppers
planted deeply within us all.

I know - silly right? Why would people be poor then?
Mama said, there was another boat
on its way, coming to pick animals.
People were not welcome.
We had to sneak on to get to paradise.

In order to reach paradise we had to pass the Banker,
the Omnipotent,
more powerful than any hyperinflation
more powerful than bankruptcy.
She was too afraid to leave,
so I head through Exodus alone.
I meet those who had previously passed.

That's why I'm practising my English,
so I can be an alien.

Lessia Mbala, Year 10

Prayers for Deadbeat Fathers

Prayers for children trying to piece together their father's
    face with nothing but fragmented memory,
prayers for mothers left to bring up children alone whilst
    battling to stay out of poverty,
prayers for young boys whose only influences are broken
    syringes and half-smoked blunts invading the spaces
    around them,
prayers for the so-called 'fathers' whose dreams are
    haunted by the cries of their children,
prayers for men sprayed in Roberto Cavalli and still carry
    a stench of worthlessness,
prayers for men who've had their two minutes of joy but
    refuse to acknowledge the product
prayers for the young girls whose mother's boyfriends
    sneak into their rooms at night,
prayers for mothers whose cries are stifled by pillows
    over their mouths,
prayers for eager children standing guard over phones
    waiting for a father's birthday call,
prayers for the man who hasn't been seen since the
    cutting of the umbilical cord,
prayers for the young boys whose only expression lies in
    the reflection of blades
prayers for men who know nothing of their off-spring
    because the truth was hidden under rags of clothing,
prayers for teenage girls used and abused by the boys
    they thought they loved,
prayers for the men that can't share the achievements of
    the children they should have helped to rear,
prayers for the woman walking down aisles on the arm of
    their mothers,

prayers for young men who don't treat girlfriends right
   because there was nobody there to teach them how,
prayers for the kids whose little hope is crushed by the
   face of reality,
prayers for little children who stare out of windows
   waiting for their daddy to come back home.

Reni Ogun-Coker, Year 11

Keys

You gave me the keys to the world.
You gave me time but
my arrogance shunned those keys,
confident in your love.
Arrogance, not strong enough to shatter our bonds
or snap the unbreakable chain even though
I'd burst your bubble of joy and hope.
Yet you hold your head high.

I remember you getting dressed for church
in your dark suit and tie; sophisticated always.
You'd polish your shoes to a glassy shiny layer.
You always put them on last.
You did not fail to notice the exact opposite in my attire.
Scattered across the floor like runaway broken bits.
You told me to keep order and do everything fully
and not half ….or there's no point.

Only recently your wisdom sunk in
the claws of your wisdom pull at me
executing every syllable
every phrase. All the significance and
new knowledge pumping my veins
alighting the dark caves of my stubborn emotional depth.

I also remember performing in a concert
that you dropped the world to see.
You strolled in with that smile stitched on so steadfastly
it disturbed the normal contours of your cheeks.
Two large craters on your proud face.

Dimples enlarge, expanding, inhaling the atmosphere as
    you located me.
You were the first one to stand and applaud.
The overwhelming sight of a standing ovation for me
made your smile mirror on my face too.

You let me know I lifted you.
For a change I'd put you on top
I gave you the world in those minutes
I shone
dispelling darkness, doubt, disappointment.
I made you proud in exchange for
realising all my mistakes.
The chains you had on me made me realise
how you'd forgiven
all the headaches I had given you
I am blessed.

Michael McHunu, Year 10

Male Figure

I don't remember much.
Dark-skinned, dark hair -
just a brief memory.

An old scar on your cheek.
The rough touch of a gesture.
I'm just another you.

Same eyes, same nose, same ears
but I only see you when I'm angry.
And I thank you.

I thank you for your absence.
For making me strong
enough not to care about the necessary things.
Now everything you say is vital.
Stuck in my head.

Just a brief memory.
Dark-skinned, dark hair.
I don't remember much.

Kalechi Ugboaja, Year 10

Crying Lesson:
Because I Could Not Stop for Death...

Behind these walls they're keeping you. As the automatic doors open, a foul stench rushes out at me as if been held captive for a million years. Here among the sick you lie. I've come to see my fortress, Constantine Costas – my mother.

A week ago, an ominous bank of dark clouds embedded you. An embolus swam through your arteries like a shark and parked itself in your control centre, disrupting the graceful flow of your blood. 'I'm going to church to pray for my children!' you said. 'I'll be back soon', she wasn't. If only we knew she was the one who needed our prayers.

With each step I take closer to the ward, part of me wears away. She's the last person I would expect to be here - the very last. On arrival, hardly any of me is left, and if a gust of unearthly wind from the windows gets any stronger, I'll disappear with it. The closer I get the more relentless smell of disinfectant becomes.

It's a sky blue room. There's a cloud that hides away every soul who wants their dignity protected. A bunch of ants in the far left corner glide across the floor as if in jubilation of my arrival. I can't find her ...where is she? My hearts starts to drum, until a weak, desperate voice halts the drummer's hand.

They waited four days to tell me. I waited four days before I went. I should've been there sooner. I couldn't bear to see the strongest person I know in agony. I should've been there sooner, but I couldn't escape from the reverie I had become lost in. For three consecutive days I drowned in dreams. A dream is an involuntary vision occurring when a person is asleep. These dreams were voluntary. For three nights my weeping sessions would morph into a sea of tears. I would lie there, as a dark figure passed, pushing me down deeper and deeper and deeper.

'Mum!' A smile burst its way through. I'm running to her like a dog that had been restricted all its life suddenly being let off its leash. I feel the ice box, where my heart once was, disintegrating. Everything around me begins to disappear. Faintly. I can only see my mother. Her smile lights a small candle of hope inside me. I'm clinging tightly to her and I realise that there's a lot less to cling onto. I'm smelling her. She smells so differently but I don't care. I cling onto her like it's my last chance. She tells me about the hospital and nurses, it's ironic. Eight days ago she would have been nursing the people in this ward. Now she's the patient, unable to nurse herself. A doctor who looks like he has just walked straight out of Madame Tussauds walks in, "Hello sweetie, I would just like to inform you that your mum is going to undergo an operation. The survival chance is one in a thousand." This is what the man in my dream said!

The third day, my dream was different. I was overpowered. A bright light penetrated the dark figure. I tried to close my eyes and shut it out but it overcame me. Then a gentle heavenly voice spoke: "Get up and go, for one of you is worth a thousand".

Sitting here now, watching some battle with their pens and others shedding tears for their troublesome past, I remind myself not to cry because my mum made it. She is now stronger than ever. Most importantly, I realised death comes to everyone; some run towards it, others push people against it. Mum's illness changed my perspective of life and made me the person I am today, the daughter of one in a thousand.

Anon

Your Fists
(Response to My Papa's Waltz *by Rothke)*

Your hatred crashed through the door
the pans slid from the kitchen shelves
clattering on cold tiles.
You came closer
spitting fury onto my pale face.

The whisky on your breath carried words of spite,
making me dizzy.

Battered on one knuckle
from the blow to my chin
you waltzed around my unconscious body
making me suffer blows from any object you could find
the mirror. The plates.
your fist …your fist…

Anon, Year 10

Dispatches from the Heart

The day has finally come, the day for your operation, dad. At least seven years of illness and at least four years of being on dialysis. It all started in the year 1998, the year I was born, the year you fell sick. Two years later, a stroke struck you and then in 2001 the dreaded news was broken: you are suffering from kidney failure. You need a new one. You can say that for my whole life you, have been ill. Unwell. Unhealthy.

July 2008 and finally we get the news you have a donor kidney. What glee we display as we rush over to the hospital. Whooping and leaping. Springing along, I have this worldwide grin on my face. Into the white walled, clinical-scented hospital we go, feeling the need to be near you, to celebrate this long-awaited news. Unless you have a seriously ill family member, you cannot understand how this news can bring glee to a family. While my sister and mother wait for the lift, my brother and I race each other up the stairs.

We are almost at your ward and I can taste my heart. It's warm. Pumping up and down my throat, I don't know how I will appear to you. We enter the ward and we each take one step into your room with deep breaths of blessed happiness. We win the race with the girls. We are together and united in glee. You smile and then start to cry. This is overwhelming. I can taste your tears. I weep with you. My dad, a grown man, is crying with gladness. We are over the moon and above the sun, we are gliding on clouds, we know you are safely recovering.

I give you a hug and a kiss and as a family we pray in gratitude. After the operation we are anxious. Days go by. We continue to visit, staying by your bedside until we are forced to leave. Nurses usher us out at the end of visiting hours. We cannot see enough of you.

I think back now to the small details- little things that walk the corridors of memory and have magnified in meaning. When you receive your dinner, you'd give me your dessert. Hospital food must have been better then! Eight years old and impressed by sweetness, I would look forward to my dad bequeathing me my favourite dessert, cake and custard, a small feast. I slurped happily eating a man-size pudding to match my man size joy. I recall how you'd walk around the hospital with a bag full of medicine attached to you, wheeling a drip on its cold metal legs, its transparent bag of medicine leashed to your arm like a pet dog. Day after day, we'd ask, "When are you coming back home, dad?" You must have been so weary of that persistent puerile questioning. Yet you put up with it patiently.

Your reply would be one of two, '...when I am well. When the doctors allow me to' or more frequently, the monosyllable 'soon'.

I think back now to how your recovery was going well, until we get the news that your brand new, longed-for kidney had stopped working. More sorrow, more trouble reared up like an angry animal, snarling at our contentment, filling us with fear. It wasn't responding to its new home. It was making you sick. It did not find its new home unwelcoming. You had an infection.

I am back in that dark time now, a scared young boy.

Day in, day out, we weave back and forth to the hospital, tired of the worn path, tired of the constant stress. You did everything the doctors said and you were in the hospital, a place of healing. How can you possibly become ill in a hospital? Can a hospital make you ill? More pills. More advice. More medicine. You would take more time to heal, to be liberated from the house of whispering walls and yo-yo emotions. More time until you exited that cold doctor-buzzing place and come home to feel the nude walls of our house and sink into the pink, leather chairs in the living room. More time until you would be able to relax and rest in the comfort of your own home, wrapped up in family.

They say no good comes out of people being sick but I like to think that it made you and mum closer than ever. It made me grow up. It brought us into a tight knit group.

When the kidney recovered and you responded well, we all waited for the day you'd be home where we could all be together. At last, you called mum saying, 'come and collect me'. We cheered.

I imagine the relief and liberation you felt as you finally waved off the sanitised, white, death-whispering walls and came home.

Kenneth Oyenusi, Year 11

Battle

I am battle-scarring
my mask of happiness
where silver bullets
roll down my cheek.

Javani Brown, Year 12

Strokes

She locks herself in her room
and strokes the silver blade.
The strokes become stronger and stronger.
The cuts get deeper
but not deep enough.

Beryl Eze Year 11

Let the Mourners Come

You are lying in the casket: cold, motionless, and peaceful as if you were fast asleep. But in this sleep, you lack the movement, you lack the breath you would naturally inhale; you lack life. 'Daddy's dead. Daddy is dead'– I am ten years old. Yesterday, I decided to find you.

I'm trying; I'm trying so very hard, to not need you – to not need anything from you. I'm going to convince myself that I can move on without you; that I can carry on with my life somehow, without ever getting an apology. I'll give it my all, I swear to you I will. I sweat and bleed and suffer, trying to be strong enough to do this without you. I told everyone around me that I was over what you had done to me; that I was over needing anything from you. I told everyone - spouting and bragging about it, hoping that if I said it often enough, it would sink into my pores and seep into my heart and into my soul and into that bereft little boy that desperately needs daddy's love.

I'm trying, Dad. I tried … but I couldn't do it.

I won't do it, because the truth is that I did need you. I do need you. I longed and ached for my father. I didn't need an apology, I didn't want an apology. What I wanted, more than anything in this world, was a hug. I lived for that moment where I would find you, and you would wrap your hands around my little ten year old body and hold me tight assuring me saying: 'Andy, I love you.' Yes, I lived for that moment … and despite all of the bad, bad things that I have experienced in my life, and despite how harshly I have been beaten down and despite how I

had lost hope for everything else, I still believed in you. I believed in you, Dad.
You were so very beautiful to me, Dad.

Andrew Frimpong, Year 11

Be You

Why would you want to be someone else?
When you could be better by being yourself?
Why pretend to be someone you are not?
When you have something they haven't got?

Cheating yourself of the life that you live
deprives others of that, only you can give
you have much more to offer by being just you
than walking around in someone else's shoes

trying to live the life of another is a mistake
it is a dishonest masquerade; nothing more than a fake
be true to yourself, let your qualities show through
others will love you more for being just you

Remember that God loves you just as you are
to him you are already a bright shining star
family and friends will love you more too
if you spent time practising just being you

Lexie Nyerere, Year 8

All of My Friends are Fakes

All of my friends are fakes
no one I know is real
they said they built the stakes
I told them life isn't a meal
I try not to make mistakes
but my thoughts have to always appeal

because people are roaming for ratings
and venturing for all of the wrong things.

Society's dead to me
have to have the best shoes to be free
if you have the wrong personality
this is teen struggle in Hackney
where choices are key
if you have the wrong personality
you may to face fatality
which is why
you have to open your eyes and see that
life is a puzzle and is hard for me
because
none of my friends are real
all of my friends are fake

Desmond Bakray, Year 8

Abandoned –

Behind the door you are packing your bags. It's not the first time. Your footsteps drag across the floor and your old, rusted hands unlock the door. I wonder if you're actually sad that you're leaving, but I will never know. You were never who you seemed to be. The front gate screeches and the lock clicks into place. We remain inside still as statues. You don't say goodbye.

Fatherless. I remember the day I came by to your new 'home'. I let my trembling hands knock the door. Moments passed. Its hinges squealed like elongated fingernails against a dusty chalkboard. Standing in front of me was a man with a part-grey, part-ginger beard; his shirt unbuttoned exposing the fading angry rash on his chest. He had more wrinkles than when I had last seen him. He looked at me, like I was different. I was different. Abandonment had transformed me into a new confrontational courageous me; someone brave enough to speak up.

A lump forms in my throat. Emotion chokes me; my rage mounts. You lead me inside where it's dark and ugly; stinks of stale cigarettes and this is only the hallway. Entering the living room, I am thrown back by the overwhelming wall of stench wafting from malodorous unwashed clothes, laying in clumps, waiting to ferment. I sit right across from you.

My eyes meet yours. Then all the happy memories come flooding back, washing me lovingly like a welcoming hot soapy shower on a winter morning. All those times when I would sit on the couch and you on the floor, listening to my childhood stories: all of my 'hairstyling tools' surrounding me, ready for me to play hairdresser on your hair. I loved being your daughter. I would sit on your back pretending to be a cowboy and you would be my horse. I would even pretend to feed you carrots and you'd bite my fingers instead, just to make me laugh. I was overwhelmed with what we used to be.

But all's changed now. Happy memories become just that. Memories. Gone. Buried. 'Done and dusted'. Erased by your abandonment.

It's a few minutes past ten at night and I'm waiting for you with mum. We're both waiting for you because it's my birthday and we can't cut the cake if you aren't here. My brother is already is in his room. Ten years older than I am, annoyed and realistic, he is the only one who can accept that you won't be coming home tonight. You will not come. So you let us down again. Again. Hours pass and I'm still waiting for you. Eight years old in my bright green birthday dress I finally realise that you won't help light the candles on my chocolate cake. Tears fill my eyes; I finally accept that you don't even remember my birthday. I used to think that when I asked you when my birthday was and you wouldn't reply, you were just joking. Now I realise it wasn't a joke. You have forgotten my birthday just the way you have forgotten you have a family. I take the cake outside and shove it into the garbage bin, hoping the pain will go away in the dust truck with it. It wasn't just the uneaten birthday cake that was hurled into depth of the dustbin that night. It was the hopes and tears of a disappointed eight-year-old who finally understood her father had forgotten her.

Here we are now, in your fetid living room. Your icy, voice makes me face reality. You ask me why I came. I don't respond. I avoid your gaze. I refuse to look you in the eye. I feel my eyes being dragged away from you as if some magnetic force is making them circle the space I am in; doing anything but looking at you. I am not seeing much. I note the off-white creamy paintwork peeling at the corners of the wall, the sink-filled food-crusted plates and coffee-stained cups, stacked upon one another, forming a fragile tower.

I want to be a bulldozer and smash down that tower.

Like a self-harmer, I know it will be painful to at you, so I do it. I do it because I thought I would feel something; something good and welcoming. Maybe I would have if I wasn't so upset, so afraid. So afraid of facing up to emotions I didn't want to confront: hate; disgust; anger. Confusion consumes me.

I finally tell you that I am here because I want to know how you are. I was worried about you. You don't reply. I ask why you don't ask about my brothers or about mum or anyone. Why don't you ask about us?

Words gush out of you, drowning me with intolerable pain. A tsunami of hurt engulfs me. You tell me that you don't love us; you don't even care about us or what will happen to us in the future. You don't give a second thought to my brothers and me; you don't care who we are or what will become. Perhaps I already knew this, but hearing you confirm it created a sickening feeling in my stomach as though I was being force fed a disgusting iskender lamb kebab, a dish I despise. Your words made me want to vomit. You make me want to vomit.

I ran out of the room, slamming the dirty white door, Flat B on the second floor. 'Slam' says the door. I hope its echoes will hurt your ears. You didn't notice it just like you didn't notice me. I remember walking over to the top of the staircase in the quiet corridors and sitting there silent and hurt, my arms wrapped so tightly around myself in a hug I wished would comfort me. I sat there, a fatherless child in an empty stairwell in a derelict estate area.

Abandoned like most of the houses round here. I sat there, my body gently rocking itself back and forth, cheeks stained with tears. My watery eyes attempted to release the ache of rejection. My older brother was right all along.

Aylin Olkun, Year 11

Water

Water is the relief of every broken hearted girl.
Each tear is a lesson.
Makes you wiser than before.
Makes you stronger than you know.
The dryness of each teacher engulfs her past and forms a
    remedy,
a key that opens a new heart.
Water; tears, a harmless liquid.
A liquid that has the capacity to grow you with your
    emotions.
But I no longer think of tears as a storm
but as the saviour of what is and is to come.

Damilola Balogun, Year 11

A Glint of Dangerous Beauty

Mirrors like glass razors
cuts scars on my hurting,
cracking the skin

Kenya McKenzie, Year 12

#reassurance

Your own self-portrait.
An instant click.
The process of trapping yourself in an image for ever.
The doorway to your soul.
The action that can reap regret or fame.
Hashtag reassurance.
The lightening that consumes the mind.
Let people judge your book by its cover.
Image saviour, thou art Steve Jobs.
Clicking the button, letting other people decide your fate.
The rolling pixel dice…show side sorrow or show side
    joy?

Year 10, class P1

Britain's Society

I live in a society where young boys
cradle death in their hands,
where pride is a blood spilling currency,
where fragmented screams throb and gush through
    blistered darkness.
I live in a society where hope is sold at school
but nobody's buying it.

I live in a society where Princess Di was murdered by
    media.
I live in a society where having a job doesn't save you
    from poverty.
I live in a society where the rich live next to the poor.
I live in a society where the scale of racism crescendos
further up you go in the country.

I live a society that teaches girls to be pathetic and boys
    to be patriotic.
I live in a society where adults are enslaved to work until
    they are seventy.
I live in a society where the Queen parachuted into a
    stadium.
I live in a society where politicians decide the life of the
    middle class in a verbal monopoly.
I live in a society where hope is sold at school
but nobody's buying it.

Tian Sewell Morgan, Year 11

On the Island

Stepping out of the hot, stuffy plane into the brightness, the dazzling sunlight beamed down across the burning pavement. Feeling nervous and excited, I clutched my bright red beach bag in one hand and slipped my sunglasses on with the other. Overhead I hear the scream of gulls and the cheerful chatter of small fluffy sparrows. The fiery sun glares at my skin. Taking a deep breath, I inhale the sweet floral perfume of the multi-coloured flowers and plants that populate the place.

I was in St Lucia!

I pick a white and pink flower that smells of sweet honey and plunge my face deep into its cool, damp petals. With eyes closed. I breathe in the intoxicating scent that seethed out of this magical little flower. My nose will regret ever parting with this glorious smell and enchanted, I buy the beautiful wild orchid to take with me. Pushing through the crowds of eager tourists I finally making it to my waiting parents and luggage. At the exit gate, other family members wait to greet us.

Driving out of the airport car park and into the city, I begin to drink in wondrous sights. Branches of trees bedecked with neon pinkish and red flowers, other trees laden with a colourful array of juicy mangoes and passion fruits that seem to shout 'Eat Me Now' as we whizz past. Truly, in another world, I can't believe my eyes. St Lucia was gorgeously vibrant: warm cloudless aqua blue skies and brilliant rich rainbow hues are welcoming us to this island.

Slowing down as we turn a corner we are confronted with the glistening, glassy Caribbean sea. The ocean is an incessantly sparkling dance-floor where sunlight limbos under the rippling waves. The water is multi-toned: some places show a deep warm aquamarine, others a cool green. Dark purple streaks through the waves, leaving shadows of mystery on the turquoise surface. The gleaming shore has sand that shimmers in the heat and curls around the black lava rocks that sunbathe in the mist of the splashing waves.

With great force, I jump out of my seat and run to the sand which is hot and squishy beneath my toes; my calf muscles clenched to keep balance as I pace across it. I stopped at water's edge- just before the water could kiss my waiting legs. This is Heaven. Ripping off my tee shirt, I reveal the new bathing suit underneath, bought for this moment. I was ready.

Mary-Katelyn Flanders, Year 8

London

My city holds a host of people; each one comes in a
    different shade of anger,
My city tastes of bad luck, deep curses,
My city smells of tar, lip gloss, illness,
My city is laced with the wrong paths
My city has blurred lines between the killers and those
    who die,
My city aches for all the angry young men lurking
in wrong post codes
Tempting fate
Searching for acceptance in the wrong families

My city confuses pitch black with cocaine white.
My city seeps sorrow and lost pride, crunching empty
    beer cans underfoot

My inner city is frozen in the chains of time like
respiration loosening and tightening, constricting hearts,
    and numbing minds

My city rains the debris of broken ambitions and
    fragmented dreams into its lonely alleyways
My city is constructed with a web of lies, a gossamer
    gated cage entrapping the innocent
My city stutters, stammers, slang that no one knows
My city exercises in mean estates where squinted eyes
    from boys on bikes indicate the next victim

My city is split. My city is cleft in two. The river runs
    deep

My city bears the scars of lost youth
My city listens with Dr Dre headphones that block out all
  sound
My city is dizzy with ceaseless rounds of sirens colouring
  night
with neon blue lights
My city wants to be loved but closes itself off when arms
  reach out to it

My city weeps in shadows and longs for kites that
will not fly in its sullen helicopter skies.

Joshua Izundu, Year 11

Dublin

I am home.
I am the friendly voices that bounce off cobblestone
    streets,
conducting visitors into my cultural embrace,
feeding them thoughts, laughter and memories.
I am the beating of my heart,
the *bodhran*'s rhythmic pulse
carrying echoes of flutes and fiddles,
awakening the welcome night.

I greet her each summer,
arms wide with wonder,
summer just isn't long enough.

My lungs emit crisp air, infused with the intriguing
smell of the storehouse, bringing her senses to life.

I am the constant tapping of the reeling dancers
out-out sounding wistful rain drops which drum down
    daily,
dampening nothing but her garments.
Then she is gone.

The drumming ceases but music continues.
Waiting.

Counting down the seasons till summer rises again.

I am home.

Mae Slade, Year 10

Morning Lane

The broadness of your back
beckons my feet to run to you.
My eyes are fed up kissing you.
My heart tells me to use winter's cold as an excuse to
    hold your hand.
My ears hear copper yawns of lamp post lights and
beats of long-forgotten busker dreams
floating on a polluted sky.

My mind, cautious of love's pain, dilutes conversation,
filling it with watery words, my heart doesn't want to say.
As cold caresses my cheeks, the bus comes,
cutting the ribbon of our conversation short.
Your lips are restrained,
but the contact of our eyes make my tight chest pop,
like a flare in the night.

From the window, your broad back gives me pain;
and the bus speeds me away from Morning Lane.

Tian Sewell-Morgan, Year 11

Mrs Emancipator

November 4th, 1842
Today, I felt the elation
that from a lifetime of devotion
all women are expected to wish for.
The drum, drum, drum of Tchaikovsky
marching
through their ears.

July 2nd, 1863
They tell me it was an accident.
I don't tell them that I know better.
They call it a "carriage" accident.
I call it a failed attempt on his life.
The drumming on my brain beats on.
Remedies fail. Prayers fail.
Threw a tea cup at a servant today.

December 5th, 1865
I lay awake this night
Nay, was kept
awake this night.
Attentive to his restless moans and mutterings,
"…equality in all things…"
"…nothing else before that…"
I'm sure I'd have got more attention from him.
If only I had been black.
No worries,
Tomorrow shall soon be the day
The White House too
Shall forever turn black.

April 15th, 1865

He's gone.
Our American Cousin.
The bullet
ripped
Through my resonating finger tips,
still clasped within his old weary hands.
The drumming was back.
Bringing with it an estranged darkness.

April 12th, 1865

He told me his dream.
I told him to forget it.
What silliness.
To talk of assassins and nations
assassinations...

April 29th, 1865

Received a letter from Vicky today.
she was "utterly broken-hearted".

May 20th, 1875

He locked me,
my last and only boy.
Stupid child I'll sue
for he had me kept in at Bellevue.
He thinks I've gone mad with grief.
He's right.
I have.
Men tell
me.
That I am mental.

1876
I forget the day diary.
Overdosed on Laudanum.
Bitter taste. Bitter smell.
didn't kill me.

1882 – Last Entry
I saw him again
    -   Despite my cataracts –
hovering at golden palace gates.
Tomorrow night
I'll slip out
when no one's about,
in a coma.
He needs me
to set him free.
My poor, Great Emancipator.

Princess Ashilokun, Year 12

First Enemy of State

My President?
Her President?
The fatal blow she mutilated me with.
The woe, the desolation but always poised for the press.
How dare he?
'I did not have sexual relations with that woman, Miss L.'
7 days I was sightless to the encounters you shadowed.
But strong I shall stand, plough on I must
or so I tell myself.
As that little girl can't take me on, for what I retain she
    will not possess in tenfold.
Betrayer was he, for that blue dress tainted with their
    passion.
Unwelcoming I am, towards his embrace, to tender *my*
    child.
Disgust
We enter, ladies swoon, but oh, they don't know.
I chuckle
remembering the minutes of our sensuality
cut short
by the magic pill running low.
But I stand strong, conquering the pulse of my fellow
    constituency.
But the back of my mind was the view of her searching
    the demographics of his crinkling pruned brain.

Sarah Lamin, Year 11

Dispatches from the Heart – Something Feels Wrong

It is a Saturday evening: the street lights are on; the pavement is full of mucky puddles and I am here fighting the wind. The last bit of the sun is lost deep in the distant horizon. I am going to the bus stop; there are no cars, no people and not even pigeons on the road. It's as if life has suddenly paused or even ceased to exist.

The wind is getting stronger and the rain is falling hard showering its cold shards down as I finally reach my stop. I am a solitary traveller at this bleak waiting point. Alone. Something feels wrong. I scan for signs that I share this planet with other living creatures but nothing happens. I am grateful for the sudden sharp movement of a squirrel on the scrounge. To my right there are headlights; a bus. Reaching my destination, I notice the silence again. No sound except eerie whistling wind and rustling of leaves from the dead trees. Something feels wrong. Dragging my feet along the long road to my housing estate, I am conscious it is also deserted. With a surge of energy, I run to the swings feeling them sway and down like my mood; I can't decide if I am happy or sad. Today something feels different. Something is wrong. The darkness in the sky deepens.

Then my phone rings. The screen tells me it's my friend. I answer, it's my friend's mum's voice. She starts off with the usual niceties: 'How was school? How is everything?' Her voice is starting to break as she begins to explain the real reason for her calling me. I can hear her choking back sobs as she cries through the phone: 'Chris is... d-d-dead'. I know she is seeking some comfort and reassurance from me but I am speechless. I can't help. I cannot comprehend what has taken place. I feel empty.

I listen to her heartbreak - how it happened; how her beloved, young son was left bleeding to death on a hard Hackney road while people just walked past. Frozen with horror, I can't hear anymore. I hang up and run. Running for answers. Running to make sense of things. Running for comfort. I think of the strangeness of the evening. Ominous.

I felt something was wrong.

Thinking back now, I envisage my friend, Chris, walking down his road when a group of people attacked him. Throwing him to the ground and using him as a punch-bag until one of the mob brought out a knife. I shudder as I think of the cold, sharp blade brightly shining in the dying sun. The life-thieving blade. The taker of another youth's life. I visualise the descent of this blade, delving into flesh, severing a main artery. I visualize the blood gushing out, as his cowardly attackers flee. I visualize how he was left lying there on the side of the road. He wasn't even their target. He wasn't who they had set out to kill. He was just there - an outlet for their aggression; another dead youth.

Another innocent victim of someone else's issues.

It came in like a loud crowd at a busy venue. We wanted to show we cared; people wrote messages on a wall on his block- a graffiti of grief; they lit candles; they offered condolences. For his birthday two weeks later, we gathered with speeches and memories. We shared our stories of his time with us. We tried to extract comfort from this gathering. We watched his mum and two younger brothers supporting each other.

Chris and I constantly communicated. He would send me a message. I would reply. I liked the ritual, the friendship, the two-way communication. Now as I send him a message, I know he can't reply.

Prince Kastrati, Year 11

Chanel, Cameras and Curses

In my pink Chanel suit
$32,000; tailored, of course.
My box hat, fluffy like a pink cloud
We ride out;
I'm a ride or die wife.

Dallas was hot. Marilyn Monroe was hot.
His blood splattered on me, it was hot.
His brains in my hair, my eyes;
His knowledge was now entwined in
ashes to ashes, dust to
dust.
The American Dream was now a true reality.

Yet, I weep for the camera.
I pose, I have good posture
My back is straight, my head is balanced.
He preached for equality;
'not because they are easy, but because they are hard.'

He preached, he preached
He is a martyr for America's sins.

In Air Force One, you can't take in weapons.
So why was I let in?
My duty as a First Lady was to be a witness for Johnson.
My duty as a wife was to watch my husband die.
My duty was to comfort my children, tell them that he
was murdered for America

Lee Harvey Oswald, I HATE YOU for killing him.

Jack Ruby, I HATE YOU for killing him.

America mourns for me.
America mourns for my children
America mourns for   me.
The Kennedy curse begins.
I am your national anthem.
I mourn in my pink Chanel suit.

Abigail Ajibola, Year 12

A Wise Woman.

Dear men and women,
what was our relationship like?
That I can say is entirely complicated.
The public saw what he demanded;
Our relationship was sugar coated, like a wolf in sheep's
  clothing.
I was subject to him, he was my controller, and I was his
  marionette.
I was simply a commodity, "a beautiful commodity" he
  says.
Are women no longer equal to men?
How dare he!
His affection towards me switched constantly,
Like the behaviour of a faulty light bulb.
He made me feel uneasy, unsure, undermined.
How dare he!
I resented him, I despised him, I hated him.
He didn't love me, he loved my blonde hair and blue
  eyes.
How dare he!
15 years ago, I ran into a cruel man's arms a girl,
15 years later I escape a woman.
I tell you most solemnly, that is indeed what our
  relationship was like.
Yours sincerely,
a wise woman.

Sabrina Yamoah-Afrifa, Year 12

The Participant

Stomping.
Bashing.
Looting.
Crashing;
it wasn't meant to turn out this way.
A simple protest, but they refused to listen.
You know what they say:
when you cannot be seen,
make a bigger picture;
when you are not heard
shout louder.
That is what we are doing.
I cover my face so I am not recognised,
I wear a hood so I am not known:
identity-less.
But I leave my eyes out
not only to see,
but so you can see
the windows of my soul
that is up in flames
that burns the moth eaten cloth
of the Molotov cocktail,
my fingertips cold
by the sudden rush of air that consumes
the previous space of the bottle.

I look on
as the glass splinters
and the world is set alight.

Actions speak louder than words?

Our actions, a wave of profanity and obscenity,
broadcasted around the world
so they kindle
within the eyes of the
non-identity-less.
I'd like to see the feds stop that.

I am part of the revolution,
I am revolutionary.

Lessia Mbala, Year 10

How I Miss My Father

Time waits for no one. The grey dusts of mystery ponder over the prospects of sending down rain. You are driving through the district of Umuahia and I can sense the frown on your face as you contemplate our next move. Feelings of uncertainty hang dry in the air and a herd of primitive figures scatter around our vehicle; awaiting your arrival their animosity is inexcusable. Their words of approval clatter around the body of our car in search of a way to cloud their unsuppressed rage and anger towards you and your achievements. With unquestionable precision you reverse and move on from the area. Your eyes an oil painting of a waterfall. The time is coming.

I remembered the moment you let your guard down- the split second where I was able to navigate my way into the treacherous terrains of your heart, the streets of emotional turmoil littered with ribbons of subjugation. How much I wished I understood what that simple, yet cryptic message submerged in the tears meant. The time is coming.

I vividly remember good moments we had; the joyous occasions we celebrated together- the birthdays, the graduations, the achievements. The way you would lift me up and stare into my eyes in a voiceless gesture of appreciation and pride. The way you would capture my little finger- my thumb as I used to call it when my innocence was my greatest asset. Oh, how I crave to have such moments again. Life has a funny way of responding to wishes.

You left as if you knew you weren't going to return. "I'm proud of you", you announced. "I'm proud of all of you."

You stumbled around the living room like a man drunk with helplessness and lack of belief. We urged you not to leave, not to abandon us but. You left, dad, you left me-us; all of us, from the youngest to the oldest. You left a 10 year old boy to endure the pains of life without a father. You left a 14 year old boy to be the leader of the house, you left mum to raise five children by herself in an unpleasant world we call our home. Home? It wasn't a home! I was an alien lost in the fields of eternal damnation. "Proud," I knew nothing of the word. That tabooed word which, as unfortunate as it is, is the word I would have to associate with you for the remainder of my existence.

Looking around the room, I notice my brothers, who were all smiling content and encouraged that you were showing signs of improvement. Was I the only one that knew what fate was preparing? Your promise of return would not calm my nerves.

You stride towards the door and I can't help it. Droplets of tears stream down my soft skin as you close in on the door.

Birds chirp while insects, both great and small, parade around the ground as if in honour of you. The chilled morning breeze dances around you while clouds part, welcoming the morning sun into your presence. The luscious grass beneath you sways, swatting insects away. As you stroll down the driveway closer to the cab, a period of silence commences; I'm not always a fan of clichés but if you'll allow me, you could hear a pin drop. A hum arises from the wind and is supported by the angelic choir, trees stroking their leaves together. Closer, closer to the cab. We're here. The time is coming.

We trade compliments as we bid our farewell- our final farewell. Oh, how much it hurts to reminisce about this moment. Wise eyes stared back at me with the message "I'm sorry".

I remember the moment you hugged me. Your warm hands encompassed my fragile figure. The final farewell- the last stand. You lumped yourself into the cab and it drove off. That was it. No more Daddy. No more hugs. No one else to dismiss my insecurities. No one else to call me by the name you called me, Maduka. No one else to pat me on the back. But the thing that completely shattered me was the wetness on my face. Because I knew the tears weren't mine; I'd stopped crying the moment I walked out of the door. "I love you". Those were your final words.

The date was the 11th of February 2007. How ironic, you died on the day you were born. On the 11th of February my hero was taken away from me. Daddy… gone… forever.

Darkness roars with great delight that the light of the world is gone, your heart now just a seed in the ground. A pleasant season of gladness is defiled by nature's call to rest. Even now I find it hard to believe that you are gone but stories about your bravery still revolve in my mind; that are inspiring.

How I wish I spent my time with you well. How I wish that I appreciated you while you were still alive.

Death could do us part, but memories will always cling to the fabrics of our existence. On the other side I see a tunnel void of light. As you approach, your face sparks light. Such was your personality; springing forth rivers of

119

life in places where such was unknown. Though my heart remains dark, I will always grasp onto the star that looms over the walls of it, for I know that star is you.

Chikadibia Onuba, Year 11

Rites of Passage

I was a gullible ten year old when I thought my cousin was dying.

In the mixed changing room, I remember him collapsing, though in my panicking mind, the person who I hated to love was dying. My megaphone mouth yelps for help. My lungs are pulsing; ears screaming; my heart is eddying; my nose is dribbling and my eyes are bleeding tears. I spot my Dad and the bedlam band that is my body, bolts at him. An ambulance arrived.

Tears rolled around my face like professional rhythmic gymnasts that scored zero. The life in your face rejuvenates. Bit by bit as if God had painted over a lively layer of flesh-tone acrylic in front of me. I look at you in disdain as my dad tells me your blood sugar levels were low and you hadn't eaten all day.

I remember your long camel lips leeching on a Ribena carton and your eyes piercing this condescending look of mockery that I know so well. You sing to me 'Ahhh~ Tian, you thought I was going to die.' In pink fury, I pace away from this scene, unable to find a word to call you, searching for comeback that was never going to come. Your high-pitched cackles consume me.

I was ten when my auntie died.

This was officially my first death experience after having buried a gecko in the hot dirt of a plant, in the lobby of a Spanish hotel. Only fragmented memories remain of her funeral. The small chapel, my small family of sixty, the smooth coffin, the leaflet, her smile, the melancholic music, the artificiality of uplifting speeches. I recall the broken facade of a strong husband, the shovel of dirt, the squelch of mud in the consecrated ground. The cousin who I loved to hate holds my hand while his juvenile facade crumbles sweetly; our halved hearts smash into each other. A massacre of mascara scarred women's faces; men seamlessly put their hearts on their sleeves. I was confused at the concept of having a party *after* a funeral. To *celebrate her life* they said. I see that now as opportunism. I stayed in eyeshot, earshot and mouth-shot of my father.

I remember having one meal at Aunty Natalie's house. My family are barbarians when it comes to eating; their stomachs are black holes that transport some of the energy they consume to the universe and the rest stock piles onto their bodies. The one image that remains with me is the freshly smoked salmon that scared me in its monstrosity, the way its vastness took up the table. Fat. Long. Vibrant. I remember saying 'see you soon' and waving to her through the sleepy darkness in the car window and never seeing her again. Except the part of her that lives in her husband's eyes.

I was eleven when my grandfather, on my dad's side, passed away.

After this day my dad kept on preaching, 'I will not let our relationship become like mine and my father's.' My father tried to repair the hole around my heart; his ogre like hands fumble with the loose ends of our relationship. He wants to spend time with me, rather than lose it. I couldn't attend Granddad's funeral but I knew those tinted Bill Cosby-black sunglasses, could not blanket the emptiness or malcontent, fires of rage blazing and blitzing, the roaring seas tearing away at my dad's soul as he was soaked into the array of efflorescent flowers that compressed distanced him even further away from his father.

The first and last time I saw Granddad I remember getting into the car and being met with the Grim Reaper himself; only with a layer of brown skin that was pulled and stretched in many places - you could see it was worn and torn with age and lacking some moisturising cream. When I hugged him, he collapsed in my arms, I was holding a corpse in my arms, and there was no depth. From that hug I could feel the thousands of pills he popped to keep walking; the arthritis that made every day a walk with the sins of the world on his shoulders. I could feel the pills that metastasized around his chest and swarmed a step closer as if they were playing Grandma's Footsteps without ever running away. I didn't know him well... I didn't know him at all. The warmth in his glistening maroon eyes transcended love in my heart that shocked me at the time. I will never forget that feeling.

I was thirteen when my neighbour, Derek, passed away.

I remember the day I was told that he had fallen asleep on his sister's couch and never woke up. I remember my mum smoking her soul to the high heavens to test if he could smell her sorrow. I remember Lily, his four year old dog, being orphaned without even knowing it; she was temporarily taken care of by another neighbour and every time the door opened she sped to her front door.

Waiting... And waiting...

Just waiting... for Derek to open the door to open again...

He never did.

'Derek – Gone – Derek's gone - he's never coming back ... he's gone.' Sorrow curled my body into a whimpering foetus who only wanted to cry because it was the only way I could cope. You were the accent that tickles my stomach, you were the cigarette smoke was never too strong. You are my first pub-lunch, you are an amateur ice-skater's knees as they balance and scuff and scurry around the rim of the ice rink; you are that striped black and pink New Look dress, you are the overgrowing bush of pink roses in your garden.

You are, and always will be, family to me.

Tian Sewell Morgan, Year 11

Pukka Chicken Shop

So basically yeah, you see this chicken and chip shop, it's so sick you know, I go there every day with the girls and always order the same thing, three wings and chips. That's what all the school kids order. Those sexy wings and chips, that salt and that spice that entices the chicken, the sweet, sweet chicken. Oh Lord, God bless chicken.

"What sauce would you like?" The climax of the preparation, said the man in the *Slum-Dog Millionaire* accent.

"Chilli sauce and burger sauce, please" I intone, trying to act all intellectual and posh, as I remind myself that I'm here getting an education. Sensational sauce squeezed upon a mountain of lightly salted chips. He tops it off with creamy fair peach coloured burger sauce and hands it to me. What is so flipping good about this food? The price? The fact that you know, you can buy a meal for a single pound that tastes madly peng?!

Walking out, I see a man in a suit going in. A man with a proper suit. You know, a white man in a black business suit wearing those mad pointy shoes going in to a chicken shop! He's probably going to buy a pizza or a burger or something, or maybe a chicken wrap... yeah a chicken wrap. Wraps are sort of like, posh people food whereas wing and chips is just main stream or for the "cool kids".

You see, the way it works around here is that the chicken and chips you order determines how wealthy you are. Status. If you order three wings and chips for £1.00 then you're probably a school kid, or someone that needs a quick meal for cheap... or you just can't afford anything expensive and extravagant like two piece chicken and chips £2.00 or £2.50 at those dumb expensive shops that bump you. But anyway back to the point, two piece chicken and chips are for those who want a more filling meal, like something to eat for dinner when you can't be bothered or again can't afford to cook it yourself.

Then we go up to the bigger meals which are usually the ones displayed in BOLD BIG electrical colours: pizza 7" for £4.00; burger and chips for £6.00 which is a bit of a waste of money when you can get it from Tesco for like a quid. Cheaper and looking at the quality of the food they sell there, healthier too.

But as all teenagers know chicken and chip shop isn't just a place you eat at; it's a way of life. I mean half the things I've seen here... you won't even believe. I mean once I saw a couple on a date in a CHICKEN AND CHIP SHOP! Not even Nandos which is pretty much as low as it gets, as far as I'm concerned but taking a girl on a date to a chicken and chip shop is a damn violation against everything that women fought for in the past! I can tell you this; if my man took me on a date to the chicken and chip shop he won't be my man anymore. Some people come for a little chat whilst eating, and some just to take advantage of these on the other side of those behind the counter which is pretty much low.

Although I don't fancy a date in the chicken shop, I remember one day when I had to go to the chip shop about five times in one day. The owners probably thought I had evolved into an ape or something, and there was no way I could tell them that the food wasn't all mine. Anyway back to the main. So as I was saying I went five times in five different times of the day and what and I saw was pretty epic, so in the mid-morning it was calm, a very soothing atmosphere birds chirping, kids singing ...LOL no I'm gassing. This is Hackney we don't get that here. But it was still calm. I then went in to order my food, went out very fast and that was the end of that. The second time I went to it was pretty much the same thing but the third time was a different story. It was around three, three-thirty. I entered my second home and there was a family of intruders, running around a place that was almost heavenly two and half hours ago. A mother in a pink tracksuit and about six kids all different races an all. SKET. She ordered a family bucket for seven quid gave the man tenner and waited for her meal to be prepared.

Around 15 minutes passed and that's when it all began... The complaining.

"Where's my order man?" She demanded. I just watched her in disgust as I thought about what a fantastic role model she was to her kids

"Where the hell is my order?"

She continued with a look of antipathy and impatience smothered like mayonnaise on her tomato sauce face. The men behind the counter began to work fast in the kitchen as they struggled to place the food in the buckets and give it to the chavy looking woman and her disorientated children.

"FINALLY!" she screamed.

My jaw dropped. It was like a scene off of *Eastenders* right in front of my eyes. She swung the door open walked out as her hungry rebels followed her, saliva drooling out of their mouths like savage dogs.

Let's jump to the last time of the day I went to the chicken and chip shop where all the drunk men with loose change and all the hood rats with stolen bikes come out to play. This is the worst time of day to enter a chicken and chip shop I tell you this now.

An unsanitary old drunken man hesitantly shook his change out of his pocket mumbling slurred words under alcohol breath. Two black boys watched whilst laughing at him. I stood in the background cautiously.

"W-w-why you laughing" said by the man with the blotchy green skin and alcohol ridden blood. The boy continued to laugh, "Why you f***ing laughing for huh? Stupid boys". These youths crave respect they have not earned so they flash their power to prove they're in charge, advertising their low self-esteem served with a gleam of silver.

The deadly blade swiped out as they chant curse words at the drunk. They swung the blade from left to right in front of his face but they and he show no form of fear. "What...... so you're no scared huh?" they chant, like feral beings.

All the words, echoes, screams and pleas from brown men behind counters go unheeded. They showed no mercy... no sound. The slashing sound of bloody penetration. Black boys in hoods with stolen bikes stabbed the drunk man with the blotchy skin. We stood deathly still, numbed with horror as the hyenas ran out of the shop.

Olulade Sonupe, Year 11

Afterword

'I am not a mistake; I am a complicated answer.'

This anthology is a testament to the tremendous talent of our pupils. The idea begins some time ago. Being an English teacher in Hackney for many years, I am constantly awed by the power and passion of children's writing. All the English department and school librarian, Katie Hayward, share the desire to showcase our students' writing. Their story needs to be told.

In September 2013, our bid to the Spoken Word Education Programme was successful and Raymond Antrobus became poet-in-residence. Ray is now a vital part of our English teaching team. We thank Kim Richardson of Alba Publishers whose expertise and selfless devotion of time has been invaluable. Kim worked alongside us, advising us how to get published and making it possible. Thank you, Ray and Katie for working tirelessly to get this ready for print. We are grateful to the Art Department, especially Kathryn Place, whose students designed the cover. We thank all those students, particularly Olulade Sonupe for the cover and Michael Mchunu for the title.

This writing was done in lessons, in spoken-word club, at home and anywhere our pupil-poets felt the urge to write. It is exciting to work in a place where poetry is carried in the air of corridors and congregates in classroom where pupils are brimming with 'bare words' they want to share. I am sure readers will enjoy these words and feel enchanted by the raw, beautiful, sometimes achingly personal, always fresh youthful voices.

Anne Gallagher (Head of English Department)

Acknowledgments

With thanks to the many people who made this anthology possible, especially to:

All of the pupil poets of Cardinal Pole Catholic School, 6th form Art students and pupil editors: Lessia Mbala and Amber Martin

Anne Gallagher, Raymond Antrobus, Katie Hayward, Kim Richardson, Katheryn Place, James McCrea and all of the English teachers who contributed.

Peter Kahn and all at the Spoken Word Education Programme

Jacob Sam La Rose, Michael Rosen, Toni Stuart, Joelle Taylor

Sponsors and funding for SWEP, Apples and Snakes, Arvon, Arts Council England, BFSS, KKEastside Educational Trust, Ernest Cook Trust, Goldsmiths University of London, Slambassadors UK (Poetry Society), Spread the Word and Waltham Forest Arts in Education Network.

Index of Contributors

Mchunu, Michael	77	poetry
McKenzie, Kenya	96	poetry
Moore, Chanti	32	prose
Norena, Yepez Ever	38	Spokenword
Nyerere, Lexie	90	poetry
Ogun-Coker, Reni	75	poetry
Olkun, Aylin	92	prose
Onuba, Chikadibia	117	prose
Opoku, Zoe	37	Spokenword
Osifo, Faith	44	Spokenword
Oyenusi, Kenneth	84	prose
Royer, Rhianna	22	Spokenword
Sewell Morgan, Tian prose, poetry	13,46, 98,104,121	Spokenword,
Shah, Zoia	23	prose
Shenesse, Nathan	20	Spokenword
Slade, Mae	49,103	prose
Sonupe, Olalade	39,125	Spokenword
Sowe, Isatou	19	Spokenword
Sunderland, Barrington	59	prose
Tran, Kevin	64	prose
Ugboaja, Kalechi	79	poetry
Walker, Aziel	11	Spokenword
Wei, Helen	35	Spokenword
Williams , Joanne	39	Spokenword
Williams , Jemima	41	Spokenword
Yamoah-Afrifa	61,114	poetry
Year 10 Class P1	97	poetry
Zafar, Talaya	70	prose